TALES FROM THE CRIB

CONFESSIONS OF A SHAMELESS PROCREATOR

BY HENRIK DRESCHER

A HARVEST ORIGINAL
SAN DIEGO ~ NEW YORK ~ LONDON

IN THIS BOOK:

Truths are REVEaLED

Enigmas UNRaVELED

Questions Answered

Myths DEBunKED

and Solutions OFFERED

YOU ARE ON THE VERGE OF PROCREATING YOU DONT KNOW WHY, BUT YOU FEEL A POWERFUL GENE CURRENT RUSHING YOU TOWARD AN UNCERTAIN DESTINY, AROUND YOU THE AIR IS THICK WITH BABY PROPAGANDA, THROUGH THE ROSY HAZE YOU WONDER: ARE KIDS REALLY JUST ADORABLE AFFECTION FACTORIES, OR IS THERE AN UNTOLD SINISTER SIDE TO CHILDREARING, A DARK HELL-BOUND SIDE STREET, A ONE-WAY ALLEY THAT NO ONE DARED REVEAL WHEN YOU STARTED DOWN THAT HORMONE-SPLATTERED HIGHWAY TOWARD ...

Anatomy OF a BOOBY TRAP

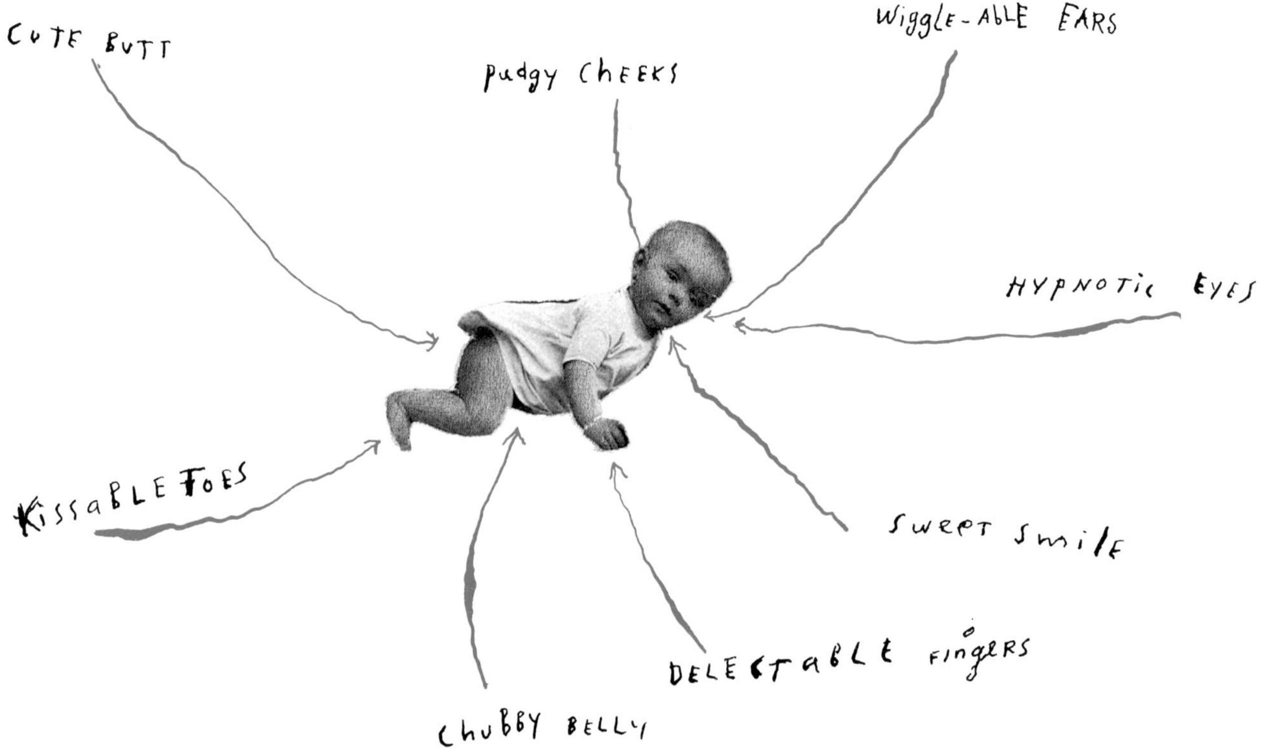

CUTE BUTT

pudgy CHEEKS

Wiggle-ABLE EARS

HYPNOTIC EYES

KISSABLE TOES

SWEET SMILE

DELECTABLE FINGERS

CHUBBY BELLY

BACHELORHOODWINKED

FUN

LOUD music

FREEDOM

UNmatched SOX

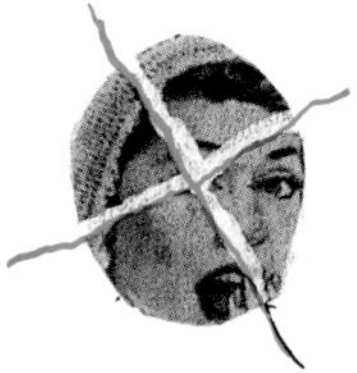

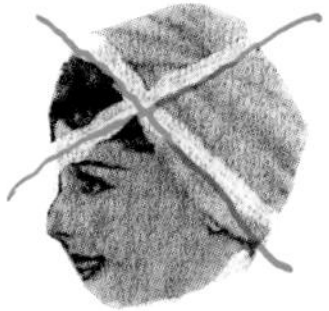

SEX
PIG
NEVER
MORE

Cigars

DIRTY LAUNDRY

LADIES' shoes

SEX

TV

DIRTY magazines

actually this is about the only thing allowed.

KISS these GOOD-BYE

REASONS to PROCREATE

You've DISCOVERED How.

YOU'RE BORED.

YOU'RE about To BREAK UP.

YOU HAVE too Little Laundry to Do.

YOU HAVE too much FREEDOM.

YOU HAVE too much MONEY.

You Feel The need to PROVE that YOU'RE ...

You're invited to a GENE pool party

consolation
FEELing

LIFE
Flushing Down The Toilet
FEELing

STRONG
Surge, PRiDe, Fatherhood
HoRmone CuRRent
within feeling

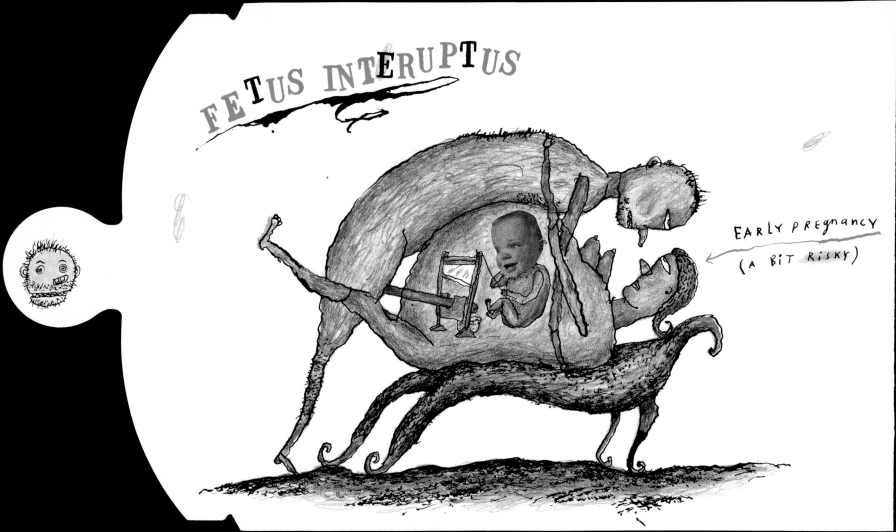

LATE PREGNANCY

(DON'T EVEN TRY)

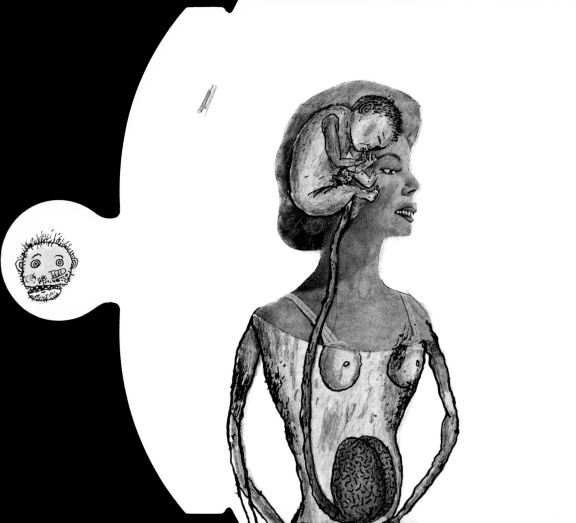

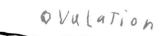

OVULATION

EVOLUTION

BRain
JACKing

IT FLOW!

WORDS TO LOOK UP IN THE DICTIONARY

EPISIOTOMY
PLACENTA
MUCUS PLUG
MECONIUM
} all these are UNDRAWABLE

LAST CIGAR

SPRINGBOARD TO THEIR FUTURE

PILLAR OF STRENGTH

VALIUM AND BEER

Small house

Big House

INVASION OF THE BODYSNATCHERS

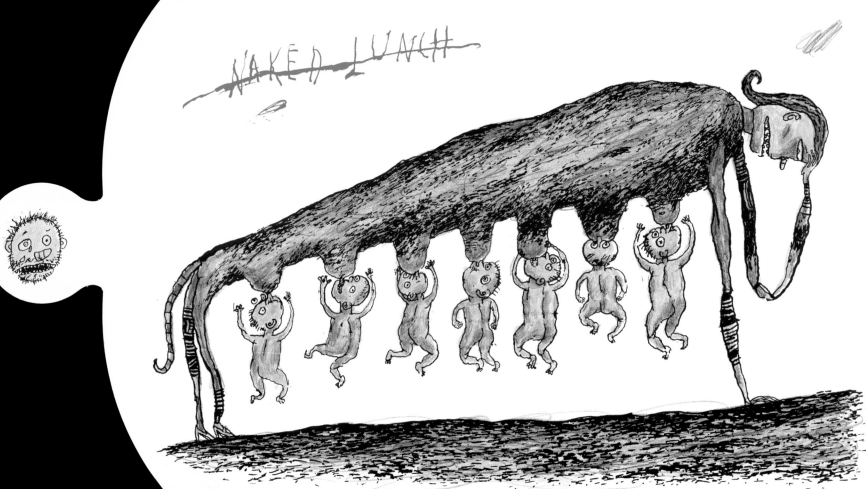

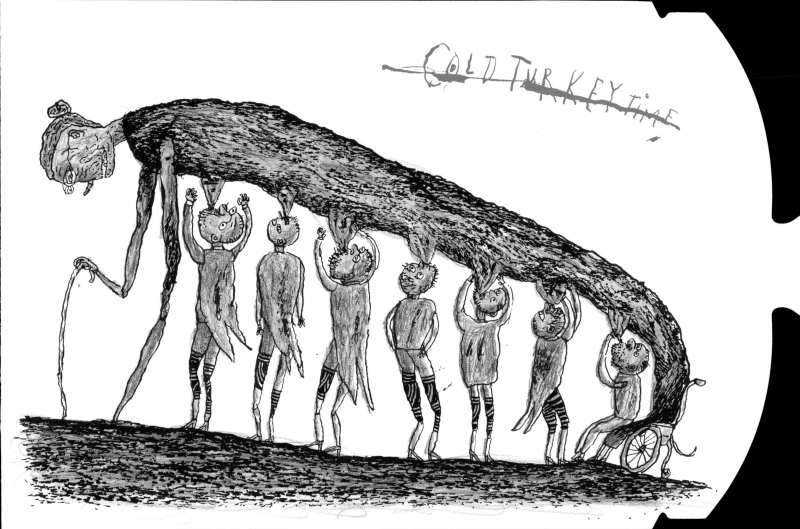

COLD TURKEY time

TEETHING

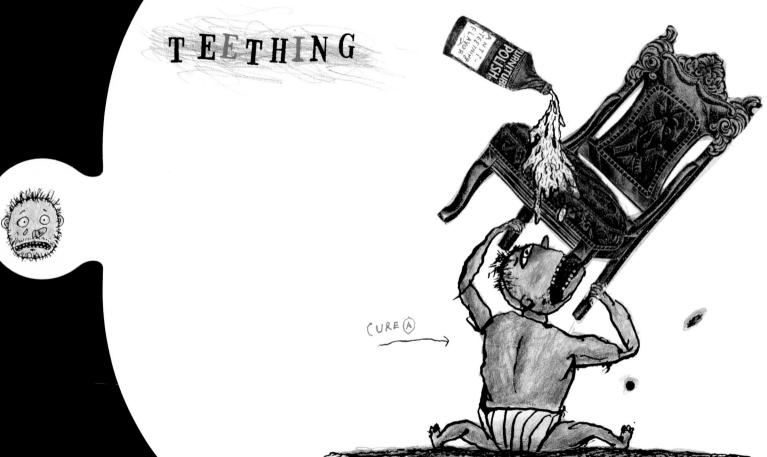

CURE B

an uncheckED
TEETHer

weaning patch.

SWITCH TO SOLID FOOD

Automatic Bibs

6-MONTH MIRACLE METAMORPHOSIS DIET

ON the FRONTIERS OF EXHAUSTION

CUDDLE HOUR

TWIN HAMMOCKS

ALmost on Empty

NATURAL BIRTH CONTROL

BEDTIME

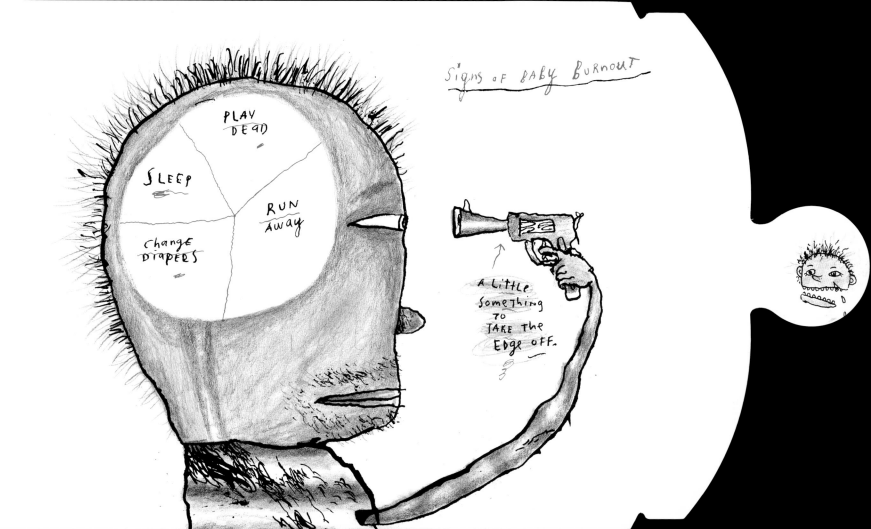

HAVE FUN ALONE!

TUNE OUT KIDS
BOND WITH TECHNOLOGY
USE HI-TECH
MACHO SPORTS
EQUIPMENT

EAR PLUGS

FREEDOM GLOVES

ESCAPE TO FREEDOM

IGNORE all attention-getting Tactics

LITTLE MIGRAINES

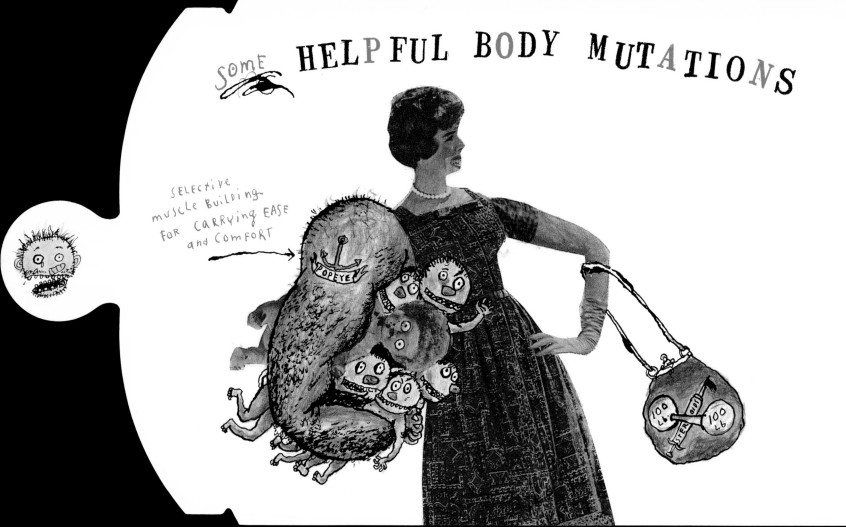

LOVELY PROTECTIVE FASHIONS FOR WORKING MOMS

← change DIAPERS and HATS SIMULTANEOUSLY!

Roll Down iRon CuRTain
DRESS SAVER

MISCELLANEOUS ATTACHMENTS
AND HOUSEHOLD HINTS

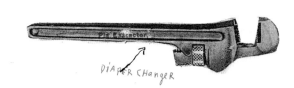

DIAPER CHANGER

WEANING MUZZLE

EAU de TOI'LET

SPONGES
TIED TO KNEES

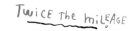

BURPS
DRIBBLE AND
EFFLUENCE

TWICE THE MILEAGE

STINKY BOTTOMS
REVERSIBLE DIAPERS

Electric Insoles
WALKING INCENTIVE

PINK
BATTERY

LAUNCH PAD

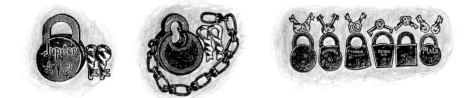

The

NOW

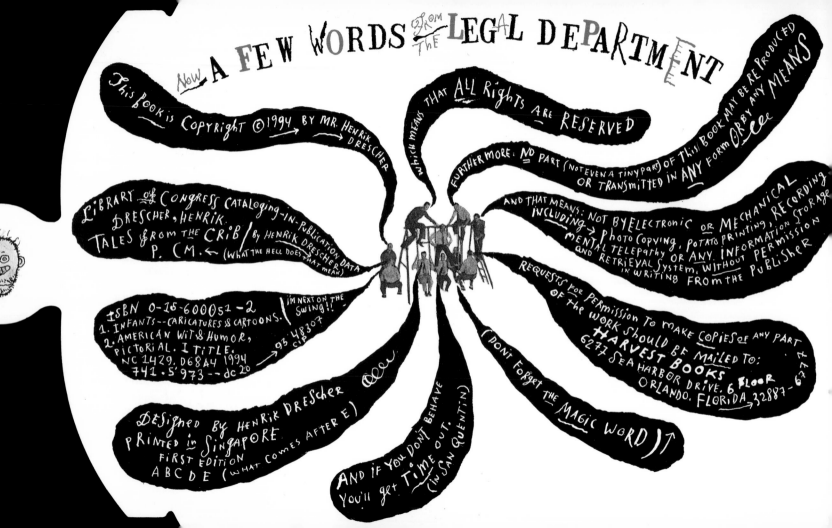

Library of Congress Cataloging-in-Publication Data
Drescher, Henrik.
Tales from the Crib / by Henrik Drescher
P. CM. ← (WHAT THE HELL DOES THAT MEAN)

ISBN 0-15-600051-2
1. INFANTS--CARICATURES & CARTOONS.
2. AMERICAN WIT & HUMOR, PICTORIAL. I TITLE.
NC 1429. D6844 1994
741.5'973 -- dc20
93-48307 CIP

(I'M NEXT ON THE SWING!!

Designed by Henrik Drescher
Printed in Singapore
FIRST EDITION
ABCDE (WHAT COMES AFTER E)

And if you don't behave you'll get TIME OUT. (IN SAN QUENTIN)